S0-ACM-721

Emily's Sister

story by
Michele Gianetti

illustrated by
Tanja Russita

proudly published by
YOUR STORIES
MATTER

First published in 2017 in England by
Your Stories Matter

Story Copyright © 2017 Michele Gianetti
Illustrations Copyright © 2017 Tanja Russita

www.yourstoriesmatter.org
hello@yourstoriesmatter.org

Your Stories Matter is an imprint of Explainer HQ Ltd
Halton Mill
Mill Lane
Lancaster
LA2 6ND
England

This book is printed in the Dyslexie font, the typeface for people with
dyslexia, though we find it great for all children. Go to
www.dyslexiefont.com to find out more about the typeface.

Fonts used on the cover are courtesy of Khrys Bosland
available from www.dafont.com

This title is available for sale online and from loads of great bookshops
worldwide.

A bulk discount is available for educational institutions and charitable
organisations through Your Stories Matter.

British Library Cataloguing in Publication Data.
A catalogue record for this book is available from the British Library.

ISBN 978-1-909320-63-5

All rights reserved by the publisher.

To Emily, you are the amazing sister Elizabeth needed all her life. God made you sisters but your efforts and love made you friends. Thank you for all you are. You are my heart.

❧

To John, thank you for your love each and everyday. It means the world to me.

❧

To my son, Michael, your ways each day with Elizabeth show so much love. You have a beautiful heart.

❧

And to my Elizabeth, you have taught us so much about life and love. Always know you are a blessing to us.

Chapter 1

Emily woke up, rolled over and then remembered!

Today is my day with Mom, she grinned. I wonder what we are going to do? And with those happy thoughts dancing behind her eyes, Emily got up.

She carefully made her bed and picked up the stuffed animals that had fallen on the floor during the

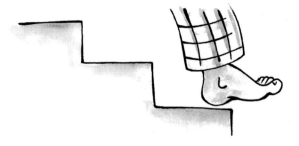

night. I've got to help Mom when I
can, Emily reminded herself.

It was then she heard her sister
crying—the reason Mom needed
Emily's help so much. Her sister was
in the kitchen with Mom, this much
Emily knew. But what was making
her cry this time? Because her sister
cried a lot! Oh well, thought Emily,
Mom will be able to calm her down
soon.

As she went downstairs, Emily's thoughts drifted to her exciting day ahead with Mom. Should they have lunch together? Or maybe a movie?

They had not been to a movie in a really long time. This was because her sister was so afraid and usually cried the whole way through.

Emily danced into the kitchen to discover the cause of this morning's tears. Mom was trying to get Elizabeth's shoes on her feet. Her sister was lying on the floor crying, with both feet sticking up in the air!

Mom looked up. "Good morning
honey, I'll get your breakfast in a
second." Mom carried on talking
calmly while struggling to get both
of Elizabeth's shoes to stay on, "I'm
always amazed how much your sister
hates her shoes!"

Mom picked up the teary-eyed
Elizabeth and carried her over to the
kitchen table, where Emily now sat
waiting.

Mom has to carry her everywhere
or she just cries and cries thought
Emily, a little sulkily. Emily asked
for waffles for breakfast. She loved
waffles.

As she watched
her Mom make
breakfast,
Emily wondered
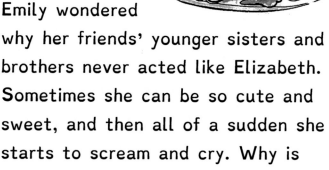
why her friends' younger sisters and
brothers never acted like Elizabeth.
Sometimes she can be so cute and
sweet, and then all of a sudden she
starts to scream and cry. Why is
that? Emily asked herself.

As Emily tucked into her waffles, she
found herself grinning at the thought
of spending time with her Mom.
Alone.

The babysitter arrived. After the
usual upset, when a crying Elizabeth
would not let go of Mom, Emily and
her Mom began their special day
together.

Chapter 2

Emily knew that the special day was ending soon, which made her feel kind of sad. The day had been so much fun!

Emily started to think about her sister again. It's weird, I missed Elizabeth being around today, but I know I can get mad at her for always crying and needing something.

If only she was happy, then I could have fun days with her too, wished Emily.

Emily recalled the fun things she had done that day. First Mom had taken her to a store to get some new clothes. Then they'd had lunch in a nice restaurant.

It had been really fun to sit with Mom and have all her attention for a change, thought Emily. Usually Mom has to focus on Elizabeth all the time just to get her to stay sitting down!

Now, Mom and Emily decided to end their special day with an afternoon at the park.

As Emily swung near Mom, she thought about how much she loved her sister—and how she wanted her to be happy rather than cry all the time.

Sometimes I wonder if I could help her more. Or maybe I could try harder to make Elizabeth happy, thought Emily a little guiltily. But I just don't know how.

Just then, she noticed her friend Matthew from school coming into the park with his younger brother and his mom. Matthew's younger brother was about Elizabeth's age. They all came over to say hi.

"Got some time just with Emily?" she overheard Matthew's mom say to her Mom. "I really don't blame you for getting away a bit. I don't know how you do it. I heard how tough it is with Elizabeth. Have you found out what is wrong with her?"

Emily didn't mean to eavesdrop, but she couldn't help hearing those words. It made her feel a bit sick.

This was her little sister they were talking about. Though hearing Mom's answer kind of helped a bit.

"Emily and I are having a special day together and it has been so much fun," Mom explained.

"We are managing with Elizabeth. She is in therapy now so things are calming down a bit. They say it is Dyspraxia and something called Sensory Processing Disorder."

Diss-PRACK-SEE-A

Wait a minute, thought Emily.
Therapy? What is that? Is that where
she goes when I sit with Mom in that
big room? Is my sister sick? Troubling
questions formed in Emily's mind.

SEN-SAW-REE
PRO-SESS-iNG
Diss-ORDER

Emily played with Matthew and his little brother for a while. But she found herself getting sadder as she watched Matthew's little brother run, play and climb. Elizabeth couldn't do those things.

Not only that, Matthew and his brother were actually talking together.

Wow! thought Emily, they are speaking so nicely to each other. Yet I find it difficult to understand

what Elizabeth says most of the time.

Maybe my sister is sick after all, concluded a very worried Emily.

After Matthew left, Mom and Emily sat down on a nearby picnic bench.

Mom turned to Emily and was just about to say something when Emily, who couldn't wait one more second, blurted out—

Mom, is ELIZABETH Sick?

Chapter 3

"Wow!" said Mom, "that is a serious question Emily. What made you ask that?"

Emily struggled to find the words to tell Mom why. She started to cry. "Mommy. So many things that Elizabeth does are ... well ... so different from Matthew's brother. He can run and play. And Mommy. He talks so well."

Emily took a deep breath, "Then I heard you tell Matthew's mom that Elizabeth has Diss-something."

Emily's Mom pulled her in for a big hug. It was now her Mom's turn to take a deep breath. "Honey, your sister Elizabeth is not sick. Please know this and believe me. Okay?"

Emily nodded and wiped away the tears from the corners of her eyes.

"Daddy and I took your sister to a special person who helped us figure out what your sister does have."

"Your sister has something called Sensory Processing Disorder, which we call SPD for short. And something else called Dyspraxia. I know those words sound strange, but I will try to help you understand."

Chapter 4

Mom continued to talk to Emily at the park. It was the first time they had talked about her sister like this. Emily felt quite grown up.

Mom told Emily that because of her sister's SPD, things that wouldn't bother most people made Elizabeth feel afraid. And the reason she cried such a lot was because when she was afraid she couldn't tell anybody— as she had not learned to talk yet.

Mom explained that because of **SPD**, loud sounds, bright lights, new foods and even going into the bathtub all felt so strange to Elizabeth's body that it scared her.

"I don't get it Mom," said Emily, "I love lying in the bath and I love to dance to loud music. So why does this happen to her?"

"Well," said Mom, "you know everyone has a brain and that the brain helps us to learn, right? Well it also controls the things we say and do."

Emily nodded.

"Your sister has a brain that has a hard time working out stuff. Like whether it is hearing, seeing or feeling a good or a bad thing," explained Mom.

"When music goes into your ears, your brain tells your body to dance. But when music goes into your sister's ears, her brain sends a message to her body that the noise is too loud. This makes her want to shut out the sound. And because she can't, she cries."

"This is what happens to your sister for many things she feels, sees and hears," finished Mom.

Emily nodded and looked down at her feet, knowing she didn't really understand. "You mean she hates everything?"

Mom smiled. "No honey, she doesn't hate everything. Her brain sends a bunch of wrong messages, making her feel nervous when they won't stop. But she doesn't hate everything."

"Remember how happy she is when we
pull up to the park?" Mom reminded
Emily. "But then she cries when
we try to get her to climb or do
something else, doesn't she?"

Emily looked up and nodded.

"Well her therapy is going to help
her do more things and enjoy them

like you do. It will help her mind and body feel a lot better."

Sitting in the park, on that fun sunny day with Mom, Emily wondered what else her sister felt like each day.

It was like Mom read her mind. "Elizabeth really does want to climb and run and play, Em. But part of what your sister has is that word beginning with D– Dyspraxia."

"It's kind of a big word, and the word isn't all that important. But it means that doing things is hard for your sister."

Emily asked, "What do you mean doing things? Doing anything? Walking even?"

"Well from what I was told by her doctor, this D-word makes most things hard for her to do," said Mom.

Emily looked confused.

"Well you know our
brains help control
all things in our
bodies, right? It
does this
by sending
signals or
messages
to parts
of the body. Each
part listens to the
message and then
does what the brain
asked it to do,"
explained Mom.

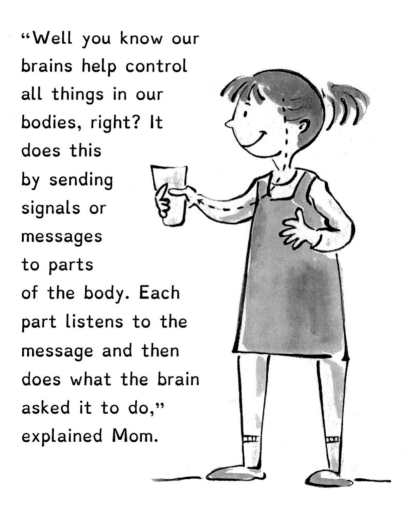

Emily remembered learning something at school about how nerves carry messages from the brain to the muscles in our arms and legs. This is how we make them move.

Mom carried on, "With this D-word, the messages the brain sends to Elizabeth's muscles don't get listened to in the right way. Kind of like the messages get muddled up."

"But her therapy," continued Mom, "will help with this too. It will help her learn how to do things that other people without Dyspraxia can already do. Therapy will help her figure out how to do things like writing, drawing and climbing steps. One day, maybe even riding a bike!"

"But why does she need to have these special lessons like she is in school?" asked Emily.

Mom said, "Elizabeth's Dyspraxia is what makes her have to learn things the rest of us can just do. But it's not like school at all!" Mom smiled. "Therapy is actually a fun place. It's like playing! But instead she is learning and getting help at the same time."

Emily thought she understood now. "I know when I have something like a cold or the flu, I get better. So will Elizabeth get better soon too?"

Mom had a sad look on her face. She looked down at her hands resting on the picnic table.

After a moment she looked up and took a deep breath, "No honey, Elizabeth will have her Sensory Processing Disorder and Dyspraxia all her life. These don't ever go away."

Then Mom looked more hopeful, "But the things we are doing, and are going to do for her, will help her deal with daily life. They'll help her body feel more comfortable. This will make her happier. I promise."

Emily started to cry a little bit, "But I don't want her to have these stupid things anymore. I want them to go away."

"So do we Emily. Daddy and I would love to make that happen. But we can't do that, so you, me and Daddy

need to know all the things we can do to help her each day. There are actually lots of things we can do."

Emily said, "So I should make her do lots of new things, right?"

"Well," said Mom, "that probably would not help her yet. She isn't ready to try lots of new things right now. And she would feel very uncomfortable if did try to make her do them."

"Instead, we can wait for the therapists to tell us when Elizabeth is ready to try new things and help with those," said Mom.

"We can encourage her. We can hug her. We can tell her we believe in her. And we can try to make each day as fun as possible. But whatever we do, Elizabeth will have some good days and some bad days."

"So she is going to stop crying a lot? Right Mom?" questioned Emily.

"I know that bothers you Emily and it makes us sad too. But yes, the therapy will help her body and brain be less afraid of things so it will help her cry less."

"And she'll be getting help to learn to talk. So, one day, she will be able to tell us what she wants or is afraid of, rather than feel the need to cry," answered Mom.

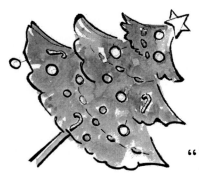

"Wow!" said Emily, "she will be better soon. Maybe even before Christmas! That will ..."

"Emily!" Mom interrupted.

"All the therapies and fun work we will be doing with her will help her grow and learn," continued Mom gently. "But I have been told that even though we will be working hard with her she won't be better by Christmas."

"We need to do these things for
quite a long time. For years rather
than weeks," said Mom seriously.

Emily looked down at the ground,
finding a stone to kick.

"Don't be sad Emily. Even though it
won't happen straight away, you will
be able to help Elizabeth learn new
things. You will be a part of how
happy she becomes!"

Emily said, "But I thought if she was better by Christmas then she would not cry at my school's Christmas play. I hate when everyone stares at us. Like at the store the other day when you had to carry her out and everyone was looking at us."

Mom looked thoughtful for a moment. She gathered up Emily's hands into her own, "I know my angel. I know how bad it makes me feel when people stare and whisper, but I didn't know that you felt bad too Emily. I am sorry honey. I promise things will get better."

"And," continued Mom, "another promise we need to make is that you promise you will talk to me or Daddy anytime, anyplace you feel sad or scared about your sister. We always want you to talk to us about your feelings, okay? I mean it Em, anytime."

"Well anytime except after bedtime!" Mom smiled.

Emily smiled too,
because they both
knew that bedtime
for Emily was a bit
of a struggle.

Mom, pleased to see Emily smiling
again, said, "Okay Emily, we seem to
have a plan don't we?"

Emily nodded her head and hugged
her Mom. "It's a plan!"

Mom reached into her purse for her phone. She leaned in and hugged Emily while pointing the phone's camera at the two of them.

"There," said Mom, "a picture of our special day together. And the day of our first real talk about your sister. I love you Emily, more than you will ever know."

Emily sat back and enjoyed feeling the warmth of both the hug and the sun at the same time. She felt much better than she had in a long long time.

I am glad I now know why she cries, thought Emily. And I am glad Mom and Daddy are getting her help. I am also very happy I know how I can help her. Yes, decided Emily, we have a plan.

Chapter 5

Emily, now 16 years old, was busy cleaning her room. Again! I cannot believe this mess is my closet, she thought.

As she was digging through whatever stuff it was she was actually digging through, she noticed a small square of wrinkled paper.

What is that? thought Emily. She reached for it and turned it over to

see the picture of her Mom and her
on the bench, that special day they'd
had their first talk about Elizabeth.

Wow! thought Emily, I remember that
day so well. And so many more grown
up talks about Elizabeth over the
years that followed.

Emily had kept her promise to talk.
And so had Mom and Dad. They'd
had plenty to talk about too—her
parents had been there for Emily
every single time.

Even though busy with Elizabeth,
Mom and Dad had made sure to make
time for Emily, cheering loudly at all
of her successes. As for her sister,
it'd been like a rollercoaster, but
Mom and Dad had given her love all
the way.

Emily sat back on her heels,
surrounded by clothes and papers,
holding the photograph lovingly.

She thought about all the new things
her sister had learned to do since
Mom had taken that picture.

Elizabeth was still learning. There were a lot of things she still struggled with. But she'll get there, thought Emily, because she's so strong and amazing!

It just takes time, and an understanding of how she learns, to help her.

I took the time to learn and found my sister, smiled Emily, and now we are the best of friends!

I sound like one of her therapists, Emily thought to herself proudly.

I guess I kind of am though. Over the last few years I have learned how SPD and Dyspraxia affect Elizabeth. How to help and support her. And even how to help others understand her.

I remember all the therapies we did at home. All the times I helped her learn something new. And all the times I spoke for her when she couldn't.

What my sister has is pretty confusing, and she can still get upset. But understanding how she works is the biggest thing anyone can do.

This thought was suddenly loudly
interrupted by her sister.

"Em, are we going for ice cream
now?" shouted Elizabeth upstairs.
"Are you done in your piggy room
yet?"

"Elizabeth, I told you I'll come with
you when my room
is done!" Emily
yelled back,
smiling.

She thought of how her sister—who couldn't talk until she was five years old—now talks non-stop.

She thought of how her sister—who never wanted to do anything—now has a huge love of life.

She thought of how her sister—who used to cry all the time—is now the happiest person she knows.

Emily closed her eyes to take a moment to be thankful for the love between the two of them, though was instantly interrupted again.

"Em! I want to go now, I'm hungry. And it's sister time!" squealed Elizabeth.

Ah, she is using the 'sister time' card, Emily grinned. She loved how much Elizabeth looked forward to sister time.

"Emily!" shouted her sister again, "Can we go now?!"

Emily looked at her room and realised she had at least another hour left before she'd be finished tidying. Tidying my room for an hour, or ice cream now? Emily thought for half a second.

Emily took the precious photo to her dressing table and stuck it to the mirror. She smiled, turned to grab her purse and keys, then headed towards her bedroom door.

"Yes, Elizabeth, we can go now!" shouted Emily.

After a quick backwards glance at the photo, Emily headed downstairs to her sister. Her little sister who was waiting at the bottom of the stairs, purse in hand, with a huge grin on her face.

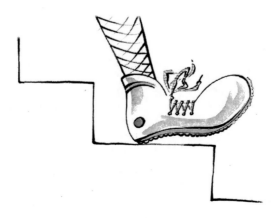

www.**YourStoriesMatter**.org

sharing experiences | improving understanding | celebrating differences

YOUR STORIES MATTER

We are independent educational book publishers
set up for social rather than financial profit:

collecting
inspiring stories
from around the world

publishing
books for schools and families
dealing with specific learning difficulties

producing
free teaching resources
that can be used with our books

YOU CAN JOIN US

as a user
of our resources to help spread well-being

as a contributor
of resources and stories to inspire others

as a champion
helping us to curate and promote info on your chosen topic

www.yourstoriesmatter.org

Some other books available from
YOUR STORIES
MATTER

You're So Clumsy Charley: This illustrated children's story (aged 6-8) explains what it feels like to be a child who is different from other children. Charley seems to keep getting into trouble all the time for doing things wrong. While not labelled in the story, Charley has a specific learning difficulty. When Charley learns he is not alone, things begin to get better for him.

Vera McLuckie and the Daydream Club: A children's story whose main characters happen to have Dyspraxia, Dyslexia and Asperger's (not made explicit). Will relate to children aged 7-9 who feel different and left out at school. The book's real purpose is one of catalyst to help parent and teacher discuss with children what it is like to have a specific learning difficulty.

The Back to Front World of Azzie Artbuckle: This illustrated children's story explains what it feels like to be a child who finds it difficult to read. When Azzie, the main character, discovers she has Dyslexia life begins to get easier for her and everyone around her. This book can be used to discuss Dyslexia and related learning difficulties with children aged 6-8.

Check them out at
www.YourStoriesMatter.org

APR 15 2018

APR 1 8 2018

CPSIA information can be obtained
at www.ICGtesting.com
Printed in the USA
LVOW10s1920280318
571478LV00012B/611/P